THE LEGEND OF THE
Cherry Queens

A VERY CHERRY FAIRY TALE

Eat your cherries!

Sally Meese "Queen of Tarts"

STORY BY Sally Meese

ILLUSTRATED BY Mollie Moody

Readers are encouraged to go to
www.MissionPointPress.com to contact the
author or to find information on how to buy
this book in bulk at a discounted rate.

 MISSION POINT PRESS

Published by Mission Point Press
2554 Chandler Rd.
Traverse City, MI 49696
(231) 421-9513
www.MissionPointPress.com

ISBN: 978-1-950659-61-6
Library of Congress Control Number: 2020909137

Printed in the United States of America

To the cherry farmers of America,
whose work is never done in bringing us
scenic beauty and morsels of joy.

The Cherry Queens' realm is cherrity.
Thank you for supporting literacy and agricultural
education with the purchase of this tale.
Proceeds from the sale of each book go to literacy programs
benefiting children and adults. For details of our giving visit our
Facebook page @Legendofthecherryqueens

Once upon a time in the Land of Delight
The cherry blossoms were blooming just right.
And people flocked from far and wide
To marvel at the wondrous sight.

The blossoms were pleased
To make people smile.
Their snowy white petals
Could be seen for miles.

Meanwhile, the farmers toiled all day and all night
To save their orchards from all kinds of blight,
From wind and rain and that nasty Frost Bite.

Then one day the Cherry Fairy
Arrived at the farm,
To protect the cherries
From all kinds of harm.

She sprinkled the grove with her magical dust
To ensure that the crop would not be a bust.

"Away with you, drought!
Away with you frost!
Away with you hail!
All you pests get lost!"

One day in spring came their greatest foe,
The cold North Wind started to blow
And all the petals came down like snow!

A blanket of white covered the ground
And now they wore nothing but sad little frowns.

The cherries had lost their crowning glory.
"But wait, don't cry, there is more to your story...
Oh, Cherries, don't worry, you are just tots.
Your real beauty awaits,
You will grow up to bring joy to lots!"

The cherries basked in the summer sun
Growing plump and juicy, every last one.
They had heard of the Cherry Jubilee
And were ready for some cherry fun!

The cherries were ripe and feeling quite proud
Their bright, red color again drew a crowd.
A little boy exclaimed in surprise,
"Look, Mommy, let's pick them for pies!"

Aghast at the thought of becoming pies,
The cherries let out a flood of cries.
The tarts and sweets wailed...

Try as she might, Fairy could not calm their fears,
The Tarts, the Sweets, the Queen Annes were in tears!
This called for help of another sort,
From the Land of Joy
Where the Cherry Queens hold court.

So Cherry Fairy set to work with her wand
And her sprinkles
And "Poof!" the Dried Cherry Queen
Appeared in a twinkle.

Dried Cherry Queen, all wrinkled and wise,
Explained they were born to be more than mere pies.

"Hush little cherries, no need to fear,
Your future is rosy and full of good cheer.
You will bring happiness to every girl and boy,
Because you are Ruby Red Morsels of Joy!"

"I summon the Queens throughout the realm,
All are needed at the helm
To join the party and share the glee:
Come to the Cherry Jubilee!"

Now each year the Cherry Queens alight
To ensure that each cherry grows just right,
And all is well in the Land of Delight!

The Tart Cherry Queen presents:

Cherry Queen Tarts

Here is what you need:

- Pie crust, home-made or store-bought
- Cherry jam, cherry preserves or cherry pie filling
- Cookie cutters
- Baking sheet, oven mitts or pot holders
- Whipped cream crown (optional)
- Red sprinkles fairy dust (optional)

Instructions:

Pre-heat your oven to 400 degrees.

Roll out your pie crust. Cut out shapes with cookie cutters. (The Cherry Queens like heart shapes :)

Lay cut-outs on a baking sheet. Put 1/2 teaspoon of cherry filling or jam in the center of each cut-out. (If you put too much on it will bubble over the edges and stick to your pan).

Bake for 6-8 minutes or until the crust is golden brown. Carefully remove from the oven with your mitts, let cool.

Add a dollop of whipped cream and sprinkles for a crowning touch if you want to be fancy.

Fascinating Facts about Cherries *

 Bees are critical for cherry blossoms to become fruit.
Cherries need bees to move pollen between flowers. That
is called pollination. Blossoms that are not pollinated fall
off the tree and do not become a cherry.

 Bees visit cherry blossoms in the morning. Cherry farmers
do not disrupt bees in the morning with loud noises.

 The average cherry tree has 7,000 cherries, enough to
make 28 pies.

 A cherry tree can be harvested in seven seconds thanks to
mechanical tree shakers.

 Not all cherry trees are grown for fruit. Some cherry trees
are grown only for their beautiful blossoms which can be
pink or white.

 Cherry blossoms that turn into fruit are always white.

 There are two main species of edible cherries: sweet (prunus avium)
and tart (prunus cerasus), also referred to as sour.

 States that grow sweet cherries are California, Washington and
Oregon, while Michigan, Utah and Wisconsin lead in
tart cherries.

 The most common types of sweet cherries are Bing, Lambert
and golden Rainier. The most common type of tart cherry is the
Montmorency. Sweet cherries are eaten fresh while tart cherries
are used in baking or turned into dried cherries.

 Traverse City, Michigan, is known as the Cherry Capital of the World.
It is the leader in tart cherry production in the USA.

 The Great Lakes region surrounding Lake Michigan has ideal
weather and soil for growing tart cherries.

 Cherries are very nutritious, jam-packed with antioxidants,
vitamins and minerals.

* Verified by Don Gregory, Chairman, Cherry Bay Orchards

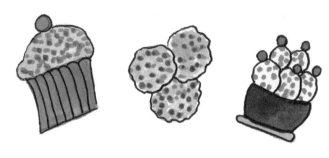

In Gratitude

I am indebted to Maggie Ellwood, my Pi Phi sister, for her original inspiration, decades-long creative support, friendship and creation of Queen Ba-Da-Bing, the tartest of them all.

And to "My" Mollie Moody, enthusiastic and energetic collaborator, and creator of the Cherry Fairy character.

In loving memory of Mollie's mother, Betty Maynard, who instilled in her a love of reading and story-telling.

A big Cherry Queen parade wave to the following friends and family who brought the Cherry Queens' legend to life every summer: Sharon and John Ritchie, Jane Nichols; Brock, Sarah and Carter Ellwood; Julie Collins, Paul Collins; Darlene, Scarlett, Henry, Harris, Carolyn and Sue Earls; Julie, John and Lindsey Mandich; Patty Brummet, Joanne Rochow, Ronna Ross, Kristie Mahoney, Andy Zoltners, Amy and Richard Schaffner, Amy and Chris Gamble, Rick Meese, Jeanne Creighton, Bill and Michelle White, Eva Feldman, Sarah Kaplan, McKenzie Sherer, Beth Bartozek, Kim Olson, Patty Barnes and Mary McKisson.

To Mary Sutherland, for making me a better storyteller.

Many thanks to all the Cherry Queens, both official and fantasy, who have served the National Cherry Festival in Traverse City, MI, and small town, Fourth of July parades.

To the children who were mesmerized by the Cherry Queens and asked curious questions that led to this story.

To my son, and Mollie's grandson, Bill, for his personal and professional words of encouragement that lit a fire under us.

And most of all to my wonderful, witty, long-suffering husband, Rick, for humoring and supporting my crazy, creative dreams.

Sally Meese